BOSTON

Our People

Coming to America

An Anthology

Sponsored by the Boston Public Library Foundation

In Collaboration with Boston Public, Parochial, and Private Schools

"Give me your tired, your poor, your huddled masses yearning to breathe free...

I lift my lamp beside the golden door."

This inscription on the Statue of Liberty underscores a philosophy that helped create the first nation in history whose population is composed almost entirely of immigrants.

Pride in one's own heritage, together with a genuine respect for the different ethnic or racial backgrounds of others, is essential to the success of the vital and diverse democracy that is America.

Diddy Cullinane, Creator
Boston Public Library Foundation/Boston Schools Collaborative Program

The Statue of Liberty

Andrea Doyle
Boston Latin High School

I consider the Boston Public Library a crucial component of our efforts to revitalize the Boston Public Schools. *Boston — Our People...Coming to America* is a fine example of what the young people of our schools can accomplish through this terrific partnership. As I'm sure you will discover for yourself, this publication showcases not only the talents of our young people but also the diversity of our residents and our neighborhoods. To everyone who has contributed to this publication, I say thank you and congratulations.

Thomas M. Menino, Mayor of Boston

On behalf of the Catholic School Communities in the city of Boston, I express gratitude to the Boston Public Library Foundation for enabling students to learn and to celebrate the value of life in a multicultural, multilingual society. The research and activities involved in the 1996 program *Boston — Our People... Coming to America* demonstrate that people from different races, cultures, and ethnic backgrounds can live in a city, retain their uniqueness, and eventually form a new common culture. Faculty and students have benefited from this unique opportunity to understand more clearly the interconnectedness of all peoples. We are proud to be involved in this collaborative educational endeavor.

Sister Ann Dominic Roach, OP, Superintendent, Archdiocese of Boston

I once heard someone say that every human being is a library, a valuable repository of information. *Boston — Our People...Coming to America* seems a perfect theme to capture the cultural richness and diversity of Boston's students and their families. This city continues to attract people from many lands, speaking many languages — all hoping for a life of greater fulfillment and peace. In transporting their heritage, they make invaluable contributions to society.

If each human being is a library, then each library is an expression of the multitude of human stories and ideas. Creative expression is fundamental to human development. The Boston Public Library's remarkable collection of books, periodicals, pictorial resources, and new technologies helps us to appreciate and engage in such uniquely human endeavors as reading, writing, drawing, speaking, and listening.

To the citizens of Boston, and especially to our children, I wish a lifetime of opportunities for creative self-expression, for enlightened learning, and for the privilege of sharing and respecting one another's cultures and values.

Thomas Payzant, Superintendent of Boston Public Schools

Contents

Introduction

For the fourth year, the Boston Public Library Foundation sponsored its increasingly popular creative writing and design program in collaboration with Boston's public, parochial, and private schools to raise awareness of the extraordinary community resource represented by the Boston Public Library.

Building upon the previous year's theme *Boston — Our City*, which concentrated on the unique historical and cultural legacy of the city of Boston, the 1996 theme was entitled *Boston — Our People...Coming to America*. Students were encouraged to study, research, illustrate, and write about the multiple backgrounds, events, symbols, and experiences involved in the migration to America, specifically Boston.

Based on grade level, the program was divided into three distinct projects, with a total of 120 students chosen to receive special recognition for their wonderful submissions.

⋆ Elementary school students designed original drawings that related to immigration to America from their own family experience or events in history.

⋆ Middle school students created original designs with captions, in either English or Spanish, which highlighted how our country became a land of many cultures and races. Winning submissions were displayed on 200 billboards located in the diverse neighborhoods of Greater Boston.

⋆ High school students wrote stories, poems, essays, and produced illustrations of the people, places, and activities involved in the many experiences associated with immigration.

On June 1, 1996, Mayor Thomas Menino and Boston Public School Superintendent Thomas Payzant joined Library Foundation Board Member Diddy Cullinane and others to honor the hard work of these award-winning students. Over 500 guests, including students, teachers, librarians, school administrators, and political and business leaders, enjoyed an awards program and a brunch held at the John F. Kennedy Library.

A very special thank you to Mrs. Teresa Heinz and the Heinz Family Foundation for endowing this collaborative program series, ensuring its continuation for years to come.

Foreword

What a pleasure to contribute my own thoughts in introduction to *Coming to America*.

As a teenager living on Governor's Island at the tip of Manhattan, I saw the Statue of Liberty every day as I went by boat to school. My little brother Jon, age 10, dressed in his Boy Scout uniform, was interviewed on the *Today* show by Dave Garroway, the two of them standing in front of that great lady, talking about America, one long-ago Fourth of July.

Like so many others, our own grandparents had come to this country from another place where life was too hard. But I doubt if Jon or I gave much thought back then to our own Norwegian immigrant ancestry. We thought of ourselves simply as *American*.

Now I look at my own family, extended by the marriages of my children, by the births of my grandchildren, and realize what a complicated and wonderful thing "being American" is. Now we have family members from Greek Orthodox, Turkish Muslim, German Catholic, and Russian Jewish cultures and traditions. My father, over ninety, bows his head each night at dinner and says a Lutheran prayer in Norwegian. One son celebrated Hanukkah as well as Christmas this year. A three-year-old granddaughter has learned her nursery rhymes in German from grandparents whose English is not fluent.

I think that's why the Statue of Liberty is smiling. She knew what it would be like and how our lives would be enriched.

Lois Lowry, Author

BOSTON

Our People

Coming to America

An Anthology

Symbols of Freedom

The People's Banner Flies on High

Kerri Vitale
Monsignor Ryan Memorial High School

America

Melissa McKeen
Monsignor Ryan Memorial High School

All around me walk those men.
They carried weapons and bombs.
No new clothes, records or those things called CD's.
Sometimes I go hungry.
Because of these men.
I have no privacy.
I share everything I have, though little do I own.
Many friends come to stay with me.
Because of those men.

One day I will have enough of this life.
Those men will not come near me
Or hinder my happiness.
Then I will become an American.
America!
Oh, what a place!
No men to harm us;
No men to steal from us anymore.
America where I am free!
Green grass and blue skies that stretch over all the land;
From coast to coast everyone is united.
Everyone is free!

That woman over there in the harbor stands,
Watching over me.
Her child.
Throughout the day and night,
She keeps the flame.

The flame of Life, Liberty, and Happiness burns,
Reminding me and all who come to see
That She is the loving mother of us all.
She protects us,
She saves us,
But most importantly, She frees us.
She is the Statue of Liberty,
The answer to all my prayers.
America!
Where I am finally free!

She Waves Her Welcome

Hubert Warno
Boston Latin High School

Ellis Island — My Grandfather's Experiences

Joseph Bosco, Catholic Memorial High School

I wonder what it must have been like to pack up whatever you could, as fast as you could, and get on a boat to go to a "new land." On top of all this, to be by yourself and at the age of twenty-three. I will never know what it must have been like, but my grandfather can paint a picture view of the entire experience.

He was in his early twenties after he fulfilled his time in the Italian Youth Military during World War II. In 1947, after seeing that he would have little opportunity for a good life in Italy, my grandfather came to America to start a new life.

Packing was tough. He wanted to bring all his things but settled only for the necessities. However, leaving was even harder. He wanted to bring all of his family, but he knew he could not, and he left by himself. After saying his good-byes and hugging his mother and sister for the last time for what eventually would be twenty years, Giuseppe Bosco crammed onto a crowded ship. For about a week he was forced to make do with what he had. This meant makeshift bathrooms, makeshift laundry rooms, and makeshift beds and bedrooms. This was only half his problem though; he had to watch out for disease. When people came to America from different countries, they carried all kinds of disease; smallpox, tuberculosis, and measles were very common.

Giuseppe's ride was tough, and if he was not careful, he could have been in trouble in a number of ways. These ships were crowded, and many times thieves or con artists tried to take what little most of the immigrants had with them. The weather conditions also played a role in the experience. If the weather was bad, everybody would have to cram inside the crowded ship. If the ship was dipping and rolling, then it would make the conditions even more treacherous. In any event, conditions were always uncomfortable. Luckily for Giuseppe, the weather on this trip was not too bad, and he could be out on deck in the fresh air.

When the approximately 3,000-mile journey was over and the ship was minutes away from docking in New York, my grandfather looked up to see the most beautiful symbol of freedom and guidance. The United States' own Statue of Liberty was standing tall and proud. He had not seen anything like it, and when he stood stunned and amazed, he knew everything would be fine. He started to think of all the opportunities to come and of his new home. He also felt awkward coming from a former enemy nation. Italy had been part of the Axis powers, an ally of Germany during World War II. Giuseppe, after thinking this, really did not know what to expect.

The ship finally docked, and the immigrants collected all their belongings, walked off the ship, and were led to an enormously large building on an island in New York Harbor known as Ellis Island. This would be something he would not soon forget. Today the name Ellis Island refers to the entire immigration center, including the buildings.

The Ellis Island experience is well documented in history. Beginning with the earliest waves of immigration in the early part of this century, Ellis Island was a major obstacle for people expecting to enter the country. In order to finally enter this country after the long, hard journey, one was subjected to questioning and medical examinations. Those people who were found to have diseases or were considered by the immigration officials as undesirable for one reason or another were either put into quarantine or sent back to their country.

One of my grandfather's problems was the fact that he did not speak English. The language barrier was a common problem for immigrants, and as a result, many family names were changed by the officials during the Ellis Island experience. My grandfather did not, however, have his name changed; it is a simple name. To his advantage, he also did not have any medical problems.

Although not having a job would present an obstacle for many immigrants, my grandfather was sponsored by an uncle. To be sponsored meant that the immigrant had someone in this country who guaranteed the government that the immigrant would have a place to live and a paying job. His job was working at his uncle's bakery located in a section of Boston known as the West End. He lived in that section of the city himself until he met Theresa Moretti, married her in 1948, and moved to a third-floor apartment in East Boston. The next big event in his "new life" was the birth of his first son, my father.

My grandfather attended college in Boston in order to learn English. Although he had graduated from a teaching college in Sicily, Italy, he was not able to get a teaching job in the United States because he did not speak English.

We must remember that although people like my grandfather were immigrants, this country was settled by immigrants, starting with colonial times. The first group of immigrants into this country were the Pilgrims escaping religious persecution. The influence of their journey set the stage for many waves of immigration. Over the years, immigrants have come to this country to escape wars, the Holocaust, famines, plagues, and the lack of opportunity in their native countries. ≡

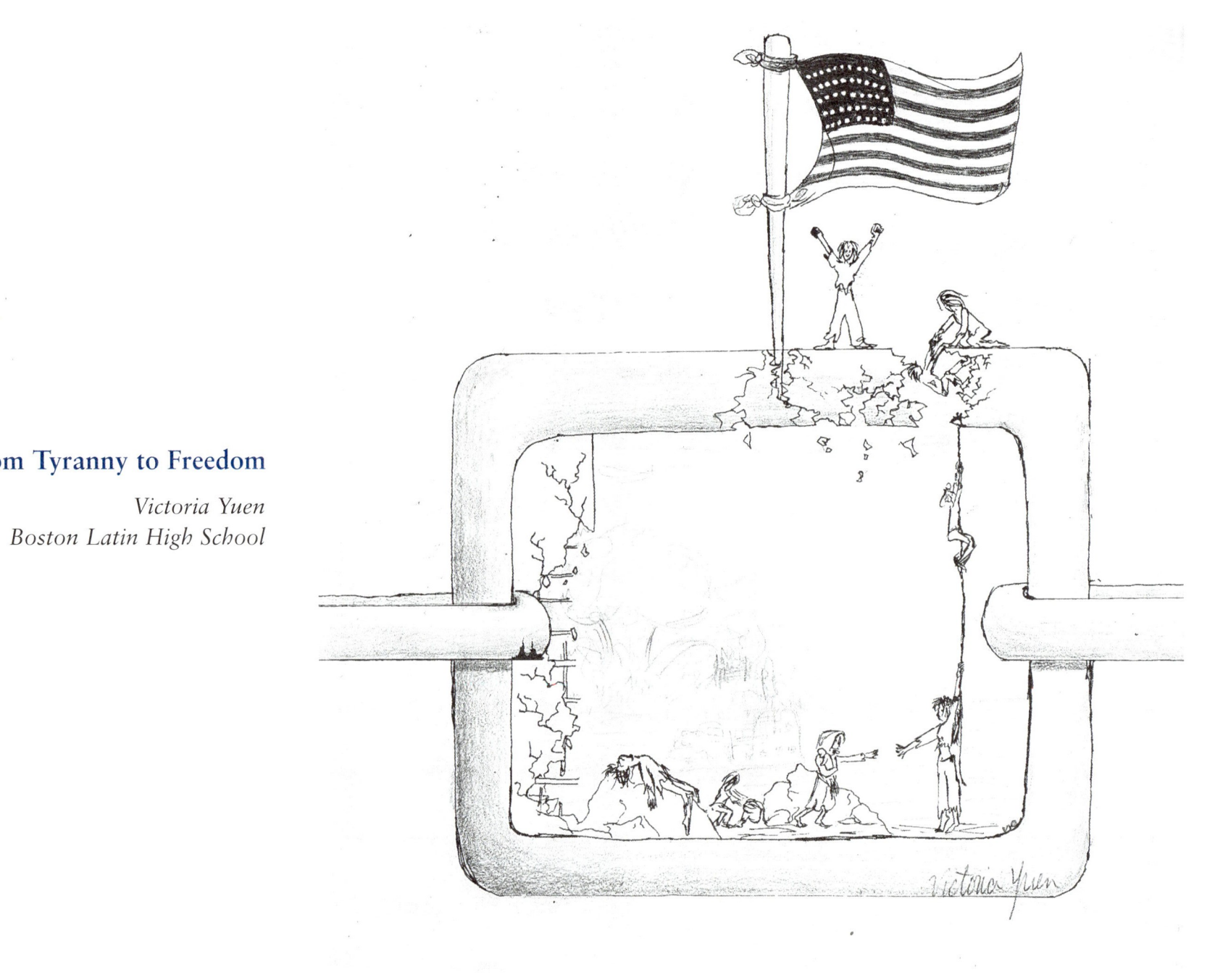

From Tyranny to Freedom

Victoria Yuen
Boston Latin High School

The Immigrant

Jessa-Leigh Stadelhofer
Monsignor Ryan Memorial High School

Crossing the sea was sick and long,
Swaying always with the waves,
I knew I would eventually see the land,
If I could endure the many days.

Looming closer in the distance,
The land of freedom beckoned,
"We will be there in a few more hours,"
The tall strong captain reckoned.

Now they're shouting the directions,
Some other language not my own,
I hold my baby close to me,
I feel incredibly alone.

Disembarking from the ship, the land supports me,
The ground screams out my name,
My soul longs to be of this land,
My heart is glad I came.

I see the statue across the harbor,
She holds her torch up just for me,
Her face is motherly and filled with peace,
She is my Lady Liberty.

We Pledge Allegiance

Zhen Quin
Boston Latin High School

The Forming of a Proud City

Kevin Chisholm, Catholic Memorial High School

On a recent visit to New York, I was able to see the Statue of Liberty, up close, for the first time. This statue is always mentioned when immigration to America is discussed. Our trip did not stop there; we bustled off the ferry, as so many immigrants did, onto Ellis Island. These historical sites made me think: people that passed the very spot I stood in the great hall made Boston the proud, hard-working city it is today. What made these people choose Boston as their place of opportunity?

Immigration in America is classified into four waves. Each one, especially the first two waves, has a bearing on the building of Boston. The first wave was the colonization period. The Massachusetts Bay Colony was a major power in the Revolutionary War. The settlers won major battles against the British in the New England area. Paul Revere, the Old North Church, and the Battle of Bunker Hill are all main historical points from the first wave of immigrants. Toward the end of the first wave, the end of slavery in the North brought the first of the African-American group to Boston.

More immigrants arrived in America as the country's popularity grew. The enormous second wave brought nearly 7.5 million immigrants to America. Almost one-third of these immigrants were Irish. So many had left Ireland because of the potato famine. Because the Irish were poor, they stayed on the East Coast — for many this meant Boston. Many consider Boston an Irish city; to see this, simply look back at former mayors and the people and places in Boston.

The third and fourth waves completed the make-up of Boston. The third wave was diverse, but the main group were the Italians. Their place in the city's history is no more evident than in the North End. The fourth wave brought mostly Mexicans and Puerto Ricans. These groups are located throughout the city. The 1990s brought a new group of people into the diverse picture. Asian immigrants, although many were already here, began arriving in the late 1970s after the Communist takeover in Vietnam, and other groups have been arriving right up to today. Like the Italians, there is a section of the city where Asian history in Boston is thriving; this place is Chinatown.

Some problems exist among these groups, as in any other place with a multi-racial population. Certain groups may have stayed in one area, but when they come together, Boston rises above other cities. Prime examples of Boston's accomplishments are its public schools, storied sports franchises, and major historic sites. Every wave of immigrants brought something special to the city. Each group that came was a stone in the foundation of Boston. Today these groups must come closer together if we are going to end the hatred and violence, because we are adding to the history of Boston made by the first residents of the city.

In closing, from the Boston Tea Party to Bill Bulger's Breakfast, from Paul Revere's Ride to Southie's St. Patrick's Day Parade, from the Boston Massacre to the ball going through Buckner's legs, from Ruth to Williams to Yaz, and from the Celtics's first championship to the sixteenth, Bostonians are proud. We are proud because we have worked hard to come this far, and we shall work even harder to become the greatest city of the future. The reason why a multitude of people chose Boston does not matter; what matters is what they did when they arrived.

Look Into the Sky

Rose Cotrone
St. Clare Central High School

Look into the sky and you will see,

It's not a bird or a plane, but it is me.

Do you recognize me, flying above you each day?

Or do you just keep going along your way?

I symbolize our country and the people who live here.

With so many nationalities, some are unclear.

There are Hispanic, German, Italian, Irish, and Greek,

And so many more with different languages to speak.

This enormous country so many of us share.

About one another, we all care.

I am the flag of red, white, and blue.

With fifty stars, and thirteen stripes, too.

I am the symbol of freedom in our land.

Where the people all stand, hand in hand.

Escapes to Freedom

Entering Boston Harbor

Phat Hoang
East Boston High School

CHOOSE: To Live in Peace or in War

Hoang Bao Nguyen
Madison Park Technical Vocational High School

In the sun!

The bright light from home, showing the way to go.

The children are crying, cause they were born into a warfare.

Where a man has killed a man. And there are people dying.

In their eyes,

The white flags are flying above.

The fears they feel inside and nobody knows just why.

The roads are destroyed, "and could they build it again?"

The economy is collapsing. Piece by piece, soon they will fall down.

"CHOOSE": To live in peace or in war?

Turning and leaving is the best they can do.

Some cross by sea, some cross by land.

It doesn't matter how they get here; get here if they can.

"AMERICA," land of the free, land of promises.

Some looked toward the future to find a better tomorrow.

"I am the newcomer. I am an immigrant."

Immigration is the art of coming to a foreign country to live and

Leave matters behind. Tears and fear, feeling down.

Headaches and memories of what was left behind.

Oh, thank God!

For lowering me down into this world to open my eyes, see, and learn

More for a mind-of-my-own paradise.

Boston is the Place to Be

Matthew Ortolaza
Amazing Grace Christian Middle School

Some Roots People Choose in America

Abisoye Babajide, Cathedral High School

Canton Avenue branched into three different streets: Paine Street, Lihtray Street, and Self Street. Paine Street was a poor neighborhood desperately reaching out for help from the rest of the world that had long forgotten it existed. Lihtray was a fairly decent neighborhood though still fighting for dreams they refused to forget. Self led to the rest of the world that had forgotten what life really was. All these streets met at Canton Avenue where day by day people, different people, dispersed into their streets, into their lives.

Paine Street was a quiet neighborhood where everyone hid in their sorrow. This was where Ming lived. She had left Vietnam to escape its poverty when she was fifteen years old, packed up like meat in a smelly refugee boat. For six years now she had been in America and had found no better luck. Ming remembered the few joys she had had with her family at the concentration camps in Vietnam: the New Year celebrations on February nineteenth and the delicious noodles her mother cooked. But even that had been lost to her in America since she had to work on February nineteenth. Here, it was one of those days that nothing special happened. Each day she wondered why she had ever felt so relieved when she got off the boat. She had once lived in constant fear of the police, but no more. What could she be afraid of now? Deportation? She felt there was nothing to lose.

Ming was working hard to earn enough money to bring her parents and younger brother to America. They put so much trust in her, and she could feel the pressure pushing her down. Ming had worked at Danny's Canning Factory, the Zinga Meat Factory, and now she was working as a maid at Hotel Fantastic. With all these changes, she still had not saved enough money. She was frustrated at the little changes she had made in the six years she had been in America. Her English was not much better, she was not married, and could see no life ahead of her. Ming had long given up on life in America. She had forgotten her dreams of prosperity and freedom, and had given up hope on her reason for being in America.

Chukwu felt trapped. He lived at the very edge of Paine Street. He came to America two years ago for higher learning. His parents worked two jobs to provide for their family's needs, including giving them a good education. Chukwu had graduated from high school five months ago, and there wasn't a single thought of going to college in his mind. He had long ago stopped thinking of the sorrow he caused his parents by making this decision. He had two younger sisters in high school.

Chukwu could not see himself as part of his family anymore, and so he finally decided to join a gang. This was the only way now he felt he could be an active, respected, and prideful member of a family and get respect from his society. Despite his parents pleading to make something of himself, he did not heed them, or rather *could* not heed them. He knew the consequences he would pay for getting *out* of the gang would be much worse than he paid in getting initiated *into* the gang. He settled into his new "cool" lifestyle in the gang, and being chased by the cops was just part of the thrill of it. However, each day he thought about the things he was missing in his life, and the things he had already lost — the culture he had been taught and raised with and held close to his heart, his religion, his respect for people, and, most importantly, respect for himself. He felt nothing better could come of his life, but it was all his decision to make. His life was in his hands, not his parents, sisters, or friends, and he knew it.

Antonio believed now that he was truly an American. He had realized long ago that becoming a citizen of America did not automatically make you an American, although it did. He lived on Lihtray Street. He had been in America for ten years and knew being here did not change his color, or his accent. He never forgot when he first came from Puerto Rico with no father or mother, with no money or support, only with a dream. He had finished high school, and now worked at Bob's Fish Market and went to night school. Antonio had struggled all these years with hardship and was now finally winning. He was one of those people who ached in hardship but never forgot or gave up on their dreams. He wanted to become a businessman and could see it a distance away. But still he looked on, knowing that some day, somehow, he would finally get there.

Joe lived on Self Street. His parents were very respectable Irish business executives. He always got everything he wanted, and to him, this was how life really was. He was twenty years old and had a car and a cool girl friend to go with it. Joe was never serious with school and never passed a class. Joe was proud of this, and amazingly, every year he still made it into the next class. Joe had not always been like this; he used to be frequently on the A list. He had once wanted to be an engineer, but after badly failing physics on a mere beginner's placement list, he gave up. He convinced himself that his dream could not be accomplished by a dumb kid like himself. Now he drank a lot and dealt drugs openly. He was known as a cool guy by some because of this, while others thought he was a stupid, ignorant kid wasting his life on pleasing people who did not care a penny for him. He blamed his parents for what he had become, but deep down inside his heart, he knew it was he who had chosen his path, who had messed up his own life.

Ming, Chukwu, Antonio, and Joe all had the power to be in control of their own lives. They all had dreams; some gave up on them and others held on even in the hardest times. These are some roads people choose in America. They branch into either Paine, Lihtray, or Self Street, all coming through Canton Avenue. They choose their path, even as we must choose ours.

America is what we make it to be. ≡

From China to Chinatown

Rui Tang Lin
Snowden International
High School

Moving On

Noreen O'Malley
Monsignor Ryan Memorial High School

When the nights grow cold, the days grow long,
And the mockingbird stops singing his song.
They know it is time to move on.

To a warmer place they must migrate,
With nothing to lead them but their dreams and fate.
Still they know they must move on.

Wanting nothing better than a better life,
Dreaming of a world with no suffering or strife,
They know they must move on.

They leave their homeland and take to the sky.
Onward toward freedom they all fly.
And they keep moving on.

Coming to America

Aly Nguyen
Taft Middle School

Jewish Immigration

Alex Garabedian, Catholic Memorial High School

During the nineteenth century European Jews were being emancipated; and in most European countries, Jews achieved some equality. At times, Jews were vilified and harassed by anti-Semitic groups. Indeed, some anti-Semites believed that Jewry was an alien race and that Jews couldn't assimilate into European cultures, but no anti-Semitic campaign was formed.

During the Middle Ages the Jews were persecuted in Germany just as they were in most of Christian Europe. The Jewish population was blamed for all types of problems: plagues, unsolved murders, cheating in business, and more.

Adolf Hitler believed that he could use anti-Semitism as a tool to help him become more popular. Like most extremists, Hitler was full of prejudices. His most passionate prejudice was against the Jewish people. Throughout all of his book, *Mein Kampf,* Hitler blamed the Jewish people for all of the troubles that Germany was suffering.

Hitler also argued that Jews were dangerous because they had virtually taken control of the German nation. The Jews, he believed, controlled the government, land, banks, and the press. He believed that the Jewish control of the press was most dangerous because they would use the press to tell Germans what they should think. In *Mein Kampf,* Hitler called this the "Jewish Plot."

The Nazis clearly wanted the Jews to leave Germany. But the Jewish people were too poor to travel, and Germany would not let the Jews leave with any money; so they could not enter any other European country. As Hitler's armies overran Europe, the Jewish people were taken by surprise. In each country, propaganda was used to spread the Nazi philosophy of racism and anti-Semitism. They forced countries to pass laws that resembled those in Germany in order to isolate the Jews and separate them from the rest of the people. As the war pressed on, the Jews were ignored or forgotten by most of the world. Hitler was free to do whatever he wanted.

The Jewish immigration to the United States was achieved in different stages, with a great many coming to America in the early 1900s. Unlike the Italians, who left Europe for the most part illiterate and unskilled, sixty-seven percent of the Jewish males who arrived in the early part of the twentieth century were classified as skilled workers. Most of the Jews utilized their craftsmanship in New York's garment trades. With the enormous numbers of Jews in the area, there was a rise in the establishment of kosher butchers, grocers, and neighborhood candy stores. The Jews also found opportunities for themselves in music and the theater and in the early decades of the twentieth century, they made up half the actors, popular songwriters, and song publishers in New York City. In 1924 Jews constituted sixty-four percent of the International Ladies Garment Workers Union, and as late as the 1940s they made up seventy-five percent of the Dressmakers Local 22 in New York City. The Jewish people differed from a lot of the immigrant groups. Becoming American meant a weakening rather than a strengthening of religious ties.

As economic conditions improved in the United States in the 1930s, increased numbers of Europeans began immigrating to America. The most important factor that influenced the immigration was the triumph of Fascism in Germany in 1933 and the coming of the war in Europe six years later. As the Germans annexed Austria in 1938, Czechoslovakia in 1939, and eventually conquered Poland in 1939, as well as Norway, Denmark, the Netherlands, Belgium, and France in 1940, hundreds of thousands fled the terror. Still more would have left had they been able to do so. Many who ran away were opponents of Nazism. University professors, politicians, and church leaders who opposed Hitler escaped or were thrown into prisons. Eventually many of those in prison ended up in the concentration camps, and some were executed.

Jews were the major victims of Nazism. They sought asylum in other countries. After accepting as many as they thought they could hold, the nations of the world refused to change their immigration policies. Until 1939, Hitler permitted almost all of the Jews to leave Germany if they chose to do so. Unfortunately, most could not find any country that would accept them. Before the exterminations in the concentration camps occurred, the German government approved an assault on the Jewish people on November 9 and 10, 1939. This assault resulted in beatings, store looting, and the burning of homes and hospitals. Twenty thousand people were rounded up for deportation to the concentration camps.

Even before World War II began, many Jews fled Germany. Many tried to flee during the war and were captured and sent right away to death camps. One account of the Jews fleeing Europe was on May 13, 1939, on the ship called *St. Louis*. Nine hundred and thirty Jews tried to enter the United States. Only a few were accepted, and they had to wait at least three years in Cuba before they could enter the United States. The rest had to return to Europe to find help. They were dispersed into Great Britain, France, Belgium, and Holland. Despite these atrocities, the immigration laws of the United States remained the same, and the American government made few allowances for the victims of Hitler's terrorism.

After the war, a new group of Jewish immigrants came to America. These were the people who had somehow managed to survive the concentration camps. About 150,000 people came to the United States between 1945 and 1954. Close to 12,000 people from eastern Europe settled in the Williamsburg section of Brooklyn, New York. These people were the Hasidic Jews, the most orthodox of all the orthodox people. They wear black hats and curls.

Most American Jews live in the Northeast from Washington, D.C., and northern Virginia up to Boston and southern New Hampshire. New York City has the largest population, representing twenty-five percent of the city and almost fifty percent of the American Jewish population. The second largest population lives in Los Angeles.

Immigration has grown considerably in the last twenty years as compared to the restrictionist days of the 1930s and World War II. ≡

Escape from Troubled Waters

Carlos Renderos
Boston Latin High School

Carlos M. Renteros

The Underground Railroad

Matt Hudak, Catholic Memorial High School

The flow of slaves escaping to freedom was greatly aided by the network of Whites and free Blacks that came to be known as the Underground Railroad. How the name arose is still a bit of a mystery.

The system was underground in the sense that it operated secretly out of view of the law and of slave catchers. It was a railroad in a way because it had a series of stations where people sheltered the fugitives and helped them onto the next station.

Beginning at the start of the nineteenth century, the Underground Railroad helped tens of thousands of enslaved Africans find their way to freedom. Consisting of more than forty routes leading through swamps, forests, rivers, and fields, the Underground Railroad played a major role in the abolishment of slavery.

Word of the Underground Railroad spread from plantation to plantation, first by whispers and then by outright talking and singing. Slaves were told by each other that this was the railroad to freedom. The first thing that fugitives did was to meet up with the "conductor" who started them on their treacherous journey to freedom. These conductors consisted of people called abolitionists, people who believed in the abolishment of slavery and freed Blacks. The runaway slaves were always in danger of getting caught, so for their safety they were hidden in stables, attics, storerooms, under beds, in secret passages, and in all sorts of other places. This was necessary because during the day slaves had nowhere to hide, and if they were seen they could be captured. The fugitive slaves moved from station to station at night by wagon, boat, train, and foot. Routes of travel were changed at a moment's notice, so that they could not be mapped easily.

One of the most knowledgeable and well known conductors on the Underground Railroad was Harriet Tubman. Along with the help of other conductors, she rescued over three hundred Africans from slavery in nineteen trips from the South to the North. Harriet Tubman always carried a pistol to protect her passengers. She also carried opium to quiet crying babies. When a passenger would get frightened and threaten to leave, she would raise her pistol high and say, "Dead niggers tell no tales. You go or die." Later in her life she proudly stated, "I never run my train off the track, and I never lost a passenger."

Beginning in the early 1800s, many anti-slavery societies began to form. By 1835 over 328 societies were in existence, and by 1838 the American Anti-Slavery Society had more than 1,350 associate societies around the country. These societies had a total membership of over 250,000 people. Many of these members played major roles in the Underground Railroad. Thousands of other people had stations throughout the country in which they helped slaves.

As early as 1820 the Underground Railroad established definite routes to Canada from all parts of the United States. The Canadian Anti-Slavery Society set aside town lots to accommodate the escaped slaves. At first the number of slaves entering Canada was small, but over time the number increased greatly. The figures range from 25,000 to 40,000 slaves entering Canada through the Underground Railroad. The portion of Canada most easily reached by fugitive slaves was the Lakes Region between New York and Michigan. Lower Canada was often reached through the New England states. The majority of runaways settled on the border in Canada for many reasons. The runaway slaves had little money and could not afford to move inland. Nova Scotia, which has less than one-tenth the population of Canada, today has about twelve percent of the black population. This is because one of the terminals of the Underground Railroad was in the Nova Scotia county of Gymsborough. This area is still full of black residents who are able to trace their roots to escapees on the Underground Railroad.

Because of the secrecy of the Underground Railroad's operations, it is impossible to say how many "passengers" it carried to freedom. Estimates range as high as 50,000 in the 30 years before the Civil War. Out of four million slaves, this is a small number. The very idea of this Underground Railroad, that Whites and freed Blacks were helping slaves to escape, angered southern white plantation owners. The railroad's activities increased the tensions between the North and the South. ☰

The People of Boston

Hand in Hand We're Here

Erin Griffin
Monsignor Ryan Memorial High School

Keeping Boston a Work of Art

Dixieanne James
St. Clare Central High School

People of Boston both present and past
Have built a city meant to last.

It started when people came for different
Causes and reasons, when they traveled
In different times and seasons.

Fortunately, we have a diverse mix
That brings to Boston a unique twist.
Chinese, Indian, Irish, Haitian,
Japanese, Italian, Spanish, Jamaican,
And many more to explore,
All with cultures to adore.

At times it's amazing to just sit back
And observe how our cultures interact.

English, Irish, and so much more can be the
Heritage of the person next door.

People of Boston both present and future
Will all take part in keeping Boston
a work of art.

Many Flags Make One

Keena DuBose
St. Clare Central High School

Through the Twists and Turns of Life

Patricia Latortue, Brighton High School

She sat on her white-washed colonial porch with the French doors and windows that the French left behind. From afar she saw a bicycle messenger coming up the smooth dirt road slowly, more like a crawl that is common for the country. The young man came into clear view, stopped directly in front of her stoop and said to her, *"mwen gin yon mesage pou fanmi Antenor, min le sipose a-le jounin Marie Yolene,"* which means "I have a message for the family Antenor, but it should go to Marie Yolene." She took the piece of paper and said, *"Merci!"* to the young man. Later she was saying her good-byes and stepping onto a plane to New York where her father was waiting for her patiently.

She stepped off to a new world, a world where the pace is quick and the timing is swift, to a father she didn't much like, a man that made had her leave her only true home: Haiti. Now she was to live with Murat, her father.

Small and fragile, pretty like a China doll, she was popular in New York where she first lived and then in Boston. But, should she speak in anger, she had a mouth sharp like a razor, and her tiny fists became the fists of a strong man.

Finally, she met Elysée, a fighter. No one was stronger; this attractive man had a heart full of creativity and soul, but his only savior from self-destruction was love. Now they are married, and their children have roots from Boston to Haiti and all the way back to Africa. These roots have carried them through all the twists and turns of life and will continue to flourish in the generations to come. ☰

A City of Races, of Different Faces

Faith Dela-Seshie
Amazing Grace Christian School

a city of races
      of different faces
           with many historical places.

a walk in Boston Common
      i saw George Washington
           the people's hearts he has won.

inside Faneuil Hall
      people stood proud and tall
           honored to be citizens after all.

i am black, you are white
      yellow, brown, red, it's all right
           for the better, let's unite

never settle for less
      always do what is best
           and our God will do the rest.

Roots

Mirlande Georges
Brighton High School

I write this poem for my country France.
You are my beautiful country.

I write a poem for you
Because you are my country.

France — I say the name and I think of the music, the fashionable
clothing, and the delicious thin *frites,*
the *café au lait,* and the fabulous *sorbet.*
France — I think of the small apartment in Paris, the park where I played,
the small shops where I always got a treat from the owners.
France — I remember when I used to go out with my grandfather —
everybody used to think I was such a cute *jeune fille.*

Then I came to Boston, which is my new home.
Now Boston means months of cold weather and lots of snow.
Boston — I like listening to rap, reggae, r&b, and soft rock.
Boston — I love to eat the junk food, the pizza, the burgers.

Boston also means French things, such as French *croissants,* the perfumes,
French music in the record stores, and French films.

In this poem I sing a song
I am French —
I am American —
And that's how life goes on.

Boston: Diverse/Together

Ebony Williams
Rafael Hernandez Middle School

Migration to Opportunity: My Family's Dream of a Better Life

Artie Imbriano, Catholic Memorial High School

People emigrate to different places or countries. These people are known as immigrants. Immigrants migrate to other places for many different reasons. Some people emigrate because they see opportunity elsewhere; others move because of poverty; some people just migrate to get a fresh start. Whatever the reason may be, immigrants would have a new and completely different way of life.

As for my family, my great-grandparents on my father's side were all from Italy. My great-grandfather Pasquale "Pat" and my great-grandmother Pasquellena "Lena" Imbriano emigrated to the United States of America from a small town in Naples. They sought better living conditions and opportunity. At that time in Italy, education was not available to all people. The rich and the socially privileged were guaranteed a chance at education and eventually a career that provided a comfortable life. Pat and Lena wanted more for their children. They wanted what only America offered at that time, equal opportunity. To them America was a land where you were able to have opportunity based on how hard you worked, not who your parents were.

They came by boat with only a trunk of clothes and their most valuable possessions. When they arrived in 1904, they first lived in the North End of Boston. They were not faced with any problems living in the North End, as it was generally an Italian area. They were comfortable in Boston but chose to move to East Boston. When they finally settled in East Boston, they ran into a problem. Being an immigrant, it was very difficult to find work. Pasquale worked at the Schraft Building, which housed a candy factory. The only Italian immigrants in the neighborhood, the Imbriano's did not get along with their neighbors for the first couple of years in East Boston. They were very different from their neighbors. Their customs, language, and behavior were strange to the people who lived there. Eventually, people became familiar with them and found them to be good, hard-working people. Slowly they were accepted and considered respected members of the community. Pat and Lena came to love America. They became American citizens.

My maternal great-grandfather was also from Italy. Pietro DeSimone emigrated from the city of Venice, in Italy. He moved to the United States of America in the year 1905 when he was just 19 years old. He moved with his first wife and infant baby girl to America, seeking a better life for his young family. He was very ambitious as a young man. He had many dreams and goals that would never be realized in Italy. He longed for the opportunities closed to him in his native land because his parents were poor. America, to him, was a land where he could be whatever he wanted. He could achieve his dreams and provide a decent life and, more importantly, an opportunity for his children to have all of the opportunities that were closed to him in Italy.

Shortly after his arrival, his wife became very ill and died. Pietro was left alone in a strange land with his infant daughter. Slowly he put his life back together, relatives cared for his daughter while he worked two jobs to support them. As time went on, Pietro labored as a bricklayer. He grew to be quite successful. His family introduced him to Maria, who moved to the United States at the age of 18. She and her family wanted to come to America as it was perceived as a land where the streets were paved of gold. This perception filled them with hope. Hope of a better life. Pietro and Maria fell in love and married.

After their marriage, Pietro became more successful. He donated his time and expertise as a bricklayer to help build the new Mt. Carmel Church in East Boston. In East Boston, Pietro and Maria did not run into the same problems that Pat and Lena had faced. Pietro's neighbors all respected him because he was a very good and charitable man. He helped out the community and his neighborhood whenever possible. As a bricklayer, he was not very wealthy, but by the time he had retired from the bricklaying business, he was able to buy a gas station. After a year or two of working at his own gas station, he bought his own oil business. Pietro then diversified into real estate where he was able to buy a few properties in East Boston.

After successfully immigrating to the United States of America, Pat and Pietro had very large families in the United States. They both decided to live in Boston for reasons unknown to me.

When I asked my grandparents why their parents left their homes in Italy, leaving their families behind in the old country, they told me something that I never realized and, hopefully, will never forget. They told me that America was the greatest country in the world. Their parents wanted to be a part of that greatness. ≡

His Family Was Torn Apart

Anastasia Sarantos, Brighton High School

1897 — Demetrios Panos was born in Asia Minor, Turkey. Of Turkish descent? No. Of Greek? Yes. It was because of this situation that his family was torn apart and forced to come to the United States as refugees. In other words, a holocaust erupted, and the Greeks were on the down side. It is easy to remember his talking about his life in Europe, the beautiful countryside of Asia Minor, the simple life, the crystal-clear Aegean Sea.

But now he felt only despair. To put it lightly, he had a slight resentment toward the Turks. The holocaust, he said, was a time of great sadness. Thousands of Greeks were murdered, often in their own churches. To have a firing squad in the Orthodox Church and torturing the women was beyond belief. For what reason? Because Turks are Muslim, and Greeks are Christian. It does not make any sense. As he fought to hold back the tears, he told of how his sister had been raped, and then scarified for some stupid war.

Obviously, he had no choice but to flee his home and hope to make it to a safer land, without losing his own life. The hardest task he had to face was separating from his family. His parents settled in the mainland of Greece, while he and his younger brother escaped to America. Amazingly, while on his long voyage, he told of how the Japanese merchant marines were the only ones who would stop to help refugees on capsized rafts. As they sailed across the Atlantic, he always kept in mind that he would no longer be threatened. Then finally, the most awesome landscape he ever saw came into sight. He tried to describe his feelings, as the boat glided toward Ellis Island, and he first glimpsed the "Most Beautiful Woman" in the world.

Ellis Island meant more then a new country. It meant a new home. A place where even if there was discrimination, one's life would not be taken. As he became more familiar with his surroundings, he learned of all the opportunities this young country had to offer: schooling, work, community life, and acceptance among his peers. My grandfather loved this country more than life itself.

Now, here in Boston, his descendants have found a new home in the new world to which my grandfather had come. Here in Boston we have our roots, both in American society and in our Greek heritage. ≡

New Arrival

Michelle Ann Fleming
Mount St. Joseph Academy (With special thanks to Carla Fontes)

The gangplank I walk down
People babble around me
I don't understand the man next to me
This is America, can it be?

Cars roar by, smoke in the air
People fly by, no one sees me
Colored signs flare
This is a city, can it be?

To learn the language, it's so hard
Strange sounds, odd letters, is it me?
Night after night with books and cards
This is school, can it be?

Becoming a citizen, proud and strong
The Pledge of Allegiance, they ask of me
I say it all, not one word wrong
This is being a citizen, can it be?

Now I have a job, I have friends
I have a home, I bought it, me
A movie, a restaurant, the fun never ends
This is America, can it be?

I'm here and now I see,
This is America, it can be
I am America, America is me!

A Positive Role Model for Me

Erizaris Asencio, Charlestown High School

On September 13, 1995, I met an author in person for the very first time. It was at the Boston Public Library. I met Julia Alvarez, a Dominican-American novelist and poet. She is currently an English professor at Middlebury (Vermont) College. She came to the United States (to New York) in 1960. She was ten years old at the time. Her father was a member of the underground movement to overthrow Rafael Trujillo, a dictator in the Dominican Republic from 1930 to 1961. She read excerpts from her new novel, *In Times of Butterflies*, and her new book of poems, *The Other Side — El Otro Lado*. The book reading was sponsored by Waterstone's Bookstore. My sister Nincis and Ms. Chin (journalism teacher) also attended the reading.

Ms. Alvarez's first novel was *How the Garcia Girls Lost Their Accents*, an autobiographical account of her experiences and those of her three sisters as Dominican immigrants in New York in the 1960s. Her second novel, *In Times of Butterflies*, is a fictionalized account of the Mirabal sisters' effort to overthrow Trujillo.

I think Julia Alvarez is one of the most persistent persons that I have met. I think that she does not rest until she finishes whatever novel or poem she sets out to write. I admire her for being someone who still has feelings for things that happened in the past, like remembering the details of her childhood.

My most vivid memory of Julia Alvarez is that we have something in common since we both emigrated to the United States from the Dominican Republic at the age of 10. Right now, I am imagining myself in the future when I am the same age she is now, becoming a novelist and poet just like her.

Well, only God knows for sure what will happen to me. In fact, no one knows what his or her future will be like. But one thing I can say for sure is that when I met Julia Alvarez, the way she talked, the way that she expressed her feelings, and her self-confidence in many ways represent a reflection of my own future. I truly feel that Julia Alvarez has become a very positive role model for me.

City by the Charles

Orlando Jackson
Timilty Middle School

She Follows the Freedom Trail

Carolyn Kelly
Boston Latin High School

Being an American:
Obstacles and Opportunities

I Came Back Home Crying

Roberto Ortiz, Charlestown High School

As an immigrant I face a lot of obstacles living here. But I look at that as a challenge, making me work hard for what I want to achieve in the future. First of all, I face language problems. Because I don't speak clearly or fluently in English, it's hard for me to get a job or to communicate with others. That's very important to me.

When I first came here in the seventh grade, I didn't know how to read, speak, or write in English. The first day I went to school, I came back home crying, because I couldn't understand what was going on in the classes. But I realized that if other immigrants have done it, I could do it, too. Once I start to speak English really well, I believe I'll have more advantages. I'll be able to read, write, and speak two languages. I'm going to have a better chance to get a job than people who know only one language. Also, I want to be a doctor, so I'll be able to help all people, especially those in the Spanish community, by translating and saving people's lives.

When I came here with my family, we, like other immigrants, started at the bottom. I had to work extra hard in school to learn a new language and do school work. In the family, I was the first one who really learned English the fastest. I had to go with my parents to appointments or meetings to translate for them, so I didn't have time to go out with the friends I had made. This has made me a stronger person in overcoming obstacles, not giving up, determined to finish my goals, and to help other immigrants, too

I'm proud of being an immigrant in the United States because I have so much to contribute to this country.

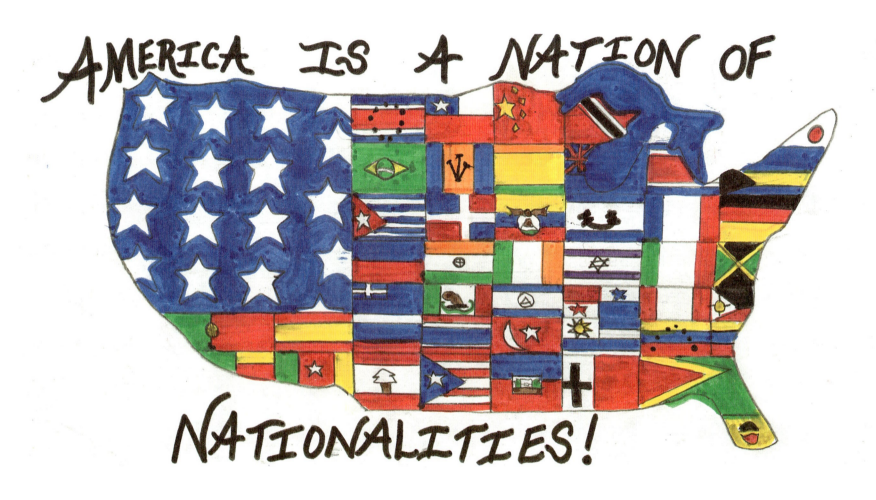

America Is a Nation of Nationalities

Julia Guzman
Sacred Heart Middle School

They Laughed at Me

Yuen-Yan Lam, Charlestown High School

"Immigrants" are people who have moved from their homelands to another country. That definition describes my family perfectly. We emigrated from Hong Kong to Boston four years ago. Since our first day here, we started a new life, just as a baby would. We could walk, but we were not familiar with the strange lifestyle and the city itself.

We had to learn the new culture and work on the new language. Our lives turned into hard times for a while. We were totally homesick. We missed our relatives, friends, and everything that reminded us of Hong Kong. At that time, I did not enjoy any single thing in Boston, especially when I had my first taste of discrimination.

I can never forget the three months that I spent at the Edwards Middle School as an eighth grade student. When I was in school, I kept my mouth shut for the whole day because I felt lonely and sad at that time. Also, I had no confidence to use my second language.

Because of my weird behavior, a group of American students always laughed at me when I passed by them. They usually said, "this fat Chinese girl does not even know a single word of English. She is dumb." I felt I had no hope in this country. I was being discriminated against. I had no friends. I did not know anything about Boston, the education system, or the American lifestyle. It was just like living in a dark corner, a dead end.

When I was drowning myself in that depressed mood, some people suddenly knocked at my door. They were immigrants who had arrived here earlier than I had. They used to have the same feelings as my family had felt. They helped me to overcome my homesickness and let me see the lighter side of this world. They became my companions who cheered me up. They helped me adapt to this world. I practiced my English. I upgraded my writing and reading skills from classes in school. My teachers encouraged me to read and listen more to English. Indeed, I gained better communication skills.

After I improved my communication skills and gained some confidence, they introduced me to some American students who were nice, generous, friendly, and willing to help me. At that time, I discovered that America was not the world of discrimination. There is only a certain minority group of people who do not like to get involved with any culture other than their own.

From that time on, I started to enjoy and appreciate the world in front of me — the land of liberty, friendly smiles, and opportunities. Today I have gained many friends from different cultures. I love to carry a smile with me. I became used to saying "How are you?" to anyone who carried the same nice smile as me, even if he or she was a stranger. I learned all these things from the American culture.

America also gives me the chance to obtain a higher educational level. I never thought about going to college when I was still in Hong Kong because there are not enough colleges over there. The opportunities available in America have totally changed my academic performance.

I hope I can prepare myself to survive in the society of the future. I shall truly try to do my best to keep my standards up and improve myself. I hope I can have the ability to show the new immigrants how beautiful America is. ▆

I Want to Look Up at the Fog-Covered Green Mountains

Xenia Calderon, Cathedral High School

"Mami, *please* tell me about Honduras." I have asked this of my mother many times over the past couple of years, as my curiosity of the world grew beyond the borders of Chelsea. In her responses, she usually emphasized all the negative aspects of her country, such as the corrupt government and the poverty perpetuated by this government.

My parents emigrated to America in the early 1970s and since have come to love this country almost unconditionally. They have almost forgotten Honduras, although the language is very alive in my household. The last time they visited Honduras together was in 1977. My mother returned in 1985 for a week to prepare my grandmother's immigration papers, *not* because she missed her country. It was business, plain and simple.

I have always wondered how my parents lived in Honduras. What streets did they walk by on their way to school, or to the market? Who was the little girl who played Barbie with my mother, and who was the boy who aided my father in causing mischief? They have answered some of these questions, but very vaguely and hesitantly. Because of the vagueness of my parents' responses, I wish I could have known my parents during their adolescence. I would then be able to observe and also experience what my parents said and did every day.

These experiences, trivial or significant, shaped my parents' identities, showing me a bit of myself. The manifestation of their identities resulted in the development of my own identity, mirroring their image.

The era and the country my parents grew up in were not perfect. *"Machismo,"* a more fierce version of sexism, was firmly established in the culture (and still is today). My parents are proof of this dogma. My father handles all the family finances; that is, he balances the checkbooks and receives and processes all the bills. My mother just recently added her name to the checking account, after about 17 years of marriage. She works from nine to five, comes home, and cooks and cleans. He expects her to serve him every night, and doesn't clean up after himself. It is like a tacit agreement. He never asks to he served, and my mother never fails to serve him.

This manifestation of the Latino culture infuriates me, although I love being a part of it. It provokes me to revolt against this injustice. As a result, I am an independent, ambitious, and self-motivated Latina, striving to conquer all adversity. I have recognized my self-worth, and express my unorthodox ideas without hesitation.

Honduras possesses a beauty unknown to the rest of the world. It is also unknown to me. I want to discover its beauty and its imperfections. I want to feel the long blades of green grass brush my legs; I want to see the Mayan ruins at Copan, and look up at the fog-covered green mountains touching the sky. I will accept its imperfections, and bask in its richness. One day, I will say to my mother: "Let *me* tell you about Honduras." ≡

Entering Boston Harbor

Amy Rugo
Boston Latin High School

Being Asian Is Unique

Ai Thi Tran, Mount St. Joseph Academy

The one experience that has affected my perspective of life happened when I least expected it. I was about nine years old and looked foreign. Foreign in the different clothes and shoes I wore, in skin, my hair, and language that I spoke. One look at me and one could assume that I was ignorant of the culture and the language. My inability to see the differences among my peers led me to a painful realization.

Being Asian is unique, but there is a high price to pay. I had to struggle through school. My classmates were all so pretty and handsome. I felt like a toad. I was dark, and my clothes looked so different from theirs. My classmates were white. They had beautiful blond hair and nice clothes. I felt ashamed of my background even more when kids started to tease me. When all of this hatred took over my life, I abandoned my native language, culture, and God.

Fortunately, I was determined and committed to work my way out of my depression. I studied very long and hard to achieve my goal, which was to learn the language and the culture. Teachers and good friends helped me. I started to show my achievements in my grades. My parents were very proud. I managed to stay on top of things in class and adapted to the new culture.

I can only remember one thing from my childhood that makes me feel resentment and bitterness. I entered the "new world" with great expectations and hope. When my first day of school started, excitement and hope turned into hatred and despair. My classmates did not talk to me; instead they laughed at me. The expressions on their faces gave me the impression that I did not belong. That moment has made an imprint in my heart ever since.

Today I have put all of these events in the past and learned that not all people are racist. I have many good friends who are different from me. I learned to love myself for who I am. I take insults better and try not to mind the ignorance of the few who do not accept me. I can say that I am lucky, and I am proud of my culture. I am working on accomplishing my big goal, which is finishing college. I work very hard to get what I have. ☰

America Is Like an Orchestra

Mary Walsh, Mount St. Joseph Academy

America can be described as many things, but for me it is like an orchestra. Each person is like an individual instrument, great played alone, but when many different instruments are played together, they are even more powerful.

Each instrument contributes its own sound, just like each person contributes his or her own culture to our nation. Each instrument is beautiful in its own way. Our audience is from Ireland, Italy, Greece, Lebanon, and all the nations and different peoples around us who listen and applaud. Many nations follow us and imitate our song, and they try to create their own.

Our conductor is the president whom we have the power to choose. This person is someone who listens and tries to understand each instrument and in the long run gains more understanding. Our song echoes in the minds and hearts of many. The poor, sick, and lonely, the rich, famous, and suffering — all listen to our song and tap their toes to the beat. Our song is one of life, liberty, and the pursuit of happiness. A song to which everyone likes to snap his fingers. ☰

An American
Collage

Rebecca Webb
Boston Latin High
School

America: A Destination Worth Reaching

Thao Thi To
Taft Middle School

My Island Home,
My Paradise

I May Never See My Paradise Again

Nyra Bannis, Brighton High School

There isn't a lot of sun in here. It feels as if something is missing. Although it might be about 85 degrees in here, outside it feels like about 20 degrees. Today is the day my father left us. I don't care if it's for the best. I don't care that we will be seeing him in a few months.

Several months ago my parents decided that they would move. I did not mind moving, of course, but this is not just moving. We are moving to America. Yes, that place that we see on TV with all the politics and violence. I'm so scared — a new school, new friends or no friends, and everything so new. It's so cold in here now.

In a few months my mother and myself are going to join my father in Boston. I have heard of Boston before, but it sounds so big. Here in the tiny island of Dominica everything is so sacred and special. Now I have to leave my tropical heaven to go to forever changing, forever snowing Boston. No more walks to the beach, dips in the river, no more hikes, no more long tropical days, no more island pudding. Oh, God, I miss it already.

My friends all seem so sad like they're really going to miss me, but I myself have seen friends come and go. I know they'll soon forget me. My best friend's name is Cerelo. We have known each other since we were very little. I am going to miss him the most. When I told him I was leaving, he kissed me on the lips. He gave me that tingling feeling like I never had before, but which I had heard my older sister talk about. Now I really don't want to leave. Now that I'm starting to look at Cerelo differently — the way he walks, the tiny perfect curls in his hair, the way his cheeks look when he smiles — I notice these things, which I never seemed to notice before. I hope he doesn't realize that I feel differently for him. It's too late now since I'm leaving.

Today is August 25, 1991, and we are leaving for the airport. I have been crying all night, and my face is sore. My eyes are red, and I truly do not want to leave. Everyone is at the airport, and it seems like a family reunion here. I feel like I am floating in a dream that will not end, and I really don't want to wake up. I cannot say good-bye to anyone anymore so I'm going to leave and get it over with. Cerelo said that he would miss me so much and that I should write to him every day; I know I will. As we board the plane, I see hands waving and familiar faces that look like the walking dead.

Now the plane is taking off, and I feel sick to my stomach because this may be the last time I see my paradise again. Hot tears roll down my face as this mechanical torturer flies away, allowing me to see above the beauty of the island where I was born and raised, my island home that I may never see again. ☰

I'll Adjust Like a Newborn Whale

Deidra Lewin
Monsignor Ryan Memorial High School

Jamaica is where the heart is,
but only for so long.

Sunny days fade, they always return,
but not my family.

I hear them from a distance,
by voice or on a telephone.

To see them, I hold close,
a framed picture once on the wall.

Home is where the heart is,
but only for so long.

I wish to be near them,
now that I'm old.

It's hard to leave the land,
I've known for so long.

But family is so special,
what we have together is special,

So I kiss the soil of my
home good-bye,

Venture on this land unknown.

I know I'm a stranger,
in this foreign land.

My accent turns heads
in the crowds.

It's all right, I'm united.

This new society, this new way
of living is different.

I'm different,
in a Jamaican way.

I'll adjust like a newborn whale
to the sea. The cold

Sets in my bones like an enemy
forcing me back to my sunlit home

Where the grass is as green
as an evergreen tree,

And the sun as rich as gold.

Here I see snow,
the first my eyes have ever seen,

And I wonder, could this be
the place for me?

Home Is the Coconut Trees and Mango Fruit

Heather Vurpillatte
Monsignor Ryan Memorial High School

Me thinks sometimes
above the noise
and confusion
I hear the sound
of silence

that takes me home
to the coconut trees
and mango fruit.
An ocean will swallow you up,
blue as the eyes
of them pretty
white ladies
in them fancy magazines.

Bored of its usual play,
the ocean beckons me,
a new toy
to pass its time.

And I go.
Now me don't smell
the sweet mango fruit
or hear the coconut trees.

Just today
the ocean
it beckoned me again.
The doorbell rang
an' there before me
stood the eyes of
them pretty white ladies
in them fancy magazines,
the ocean of deep blue.
Calling me.
I will not answer.

The Dominican Republic in Words and Picture

Phillip Perez
Don Bosco Technical High School

This picture is a representation of the country where my parents were born. My parents came to the United States because, in their country, the Dominican Republic, there were all sorts of problems. There were no jobs, no money, and a lack of education. There were many people starving and dying. My parents wanted their future children to get the best education that they could give them. It was very difficult for my parents to leave the Dominican Republic because of their loved ones. Since my mother was granted a visa, my father had to come, too. I hope this picture gives you a little understanding about my country.

Keep the Promise in "This Promised Land"

A Nation of Laws

Kelley McCarren
St. Clare Central High School

Immigration Is Our Future

Eric Irr, Kara Kelley, Ronald Pulicari, and Sean Smyth
Savio Preparatory High School

It's complete irony for a country built by and made up of immigrants to eliminate immigration. Even Native American Indians migrated here from somewhere else.

Legal immigration is our history, and it should continue to be our present and future. As the descendants of immigrants, we haven't the right to deprive these men and women of the freedom we enjoy.

Today's immigrants are having an impact on our country's culture just as the immigrants before them did. We hear exotic languages on the subway, we see exotic food on the shelves of our local markets, and we fear that our newest neighbors will take our jobs away from us. These misbeliefs were once embraced by the Anglo-Saxons of the American nineteenth century, too.

Yet now, as in the nineteenth century, many native-born Americans see immigration as something that should be restricted or even eliminated. Congress is currently debating just such issues.

Social historian John Bosnar, in his recently published history of immigration, says that many Americans are nervous about "the capacity of American society to absorb the foreign-speaking newcomers." Language seems to be at the heart of this fear.

The Language Factor

Most immigrants are usually not able to speak English when they first arrive. To meet this problem, there are ESL (English as a Second Language) programs offered in many public school districts. There are often adult education courses as well.

Though it is true that these programs cost taxpayers millions of dollars, children still need to learn English, and failure to learn can be much more expensive to the nation than education programs that work. And they do work. Most students spend an average of two years in these programs, then are mainstreamed into the school population. Often ESL programs are only necessary at the elementary school level.

Critics of immigration have a pessimistic outlook on ESL programs, but need to remember that some of these immigrants could grow up to be scientists, statespeople, teachers, and leaders of their communities.

The language difference need not automatically be a bad thing, either. Having speakers of foreign languages on our shores could be looked upon as an opportunity for the rest of us to learn more about foreign cultures. Governor and Susan Weld, in a recently published *Boston Globe* editorial, wrote that, "We look at our economy that is rapidly becoming global, and we recognize the value of speaking more than one language."

Benefits of the "Brain Drain"

America needs immigrants. They are much, much more than the villainized tax dodgers and welfare-users that critics of immigration would have us condemn.

The United States Immigration and Naturalization Service reported in 1992 that 329,321 "preference" or "choice" immigrants came to this country. Included in the category of preference immigrants are priority workers, professionals with advanced degrees, skilled workers, unskilled workers, professionals, and highly skilled immigrants.

Often foreign students decide to apply for permanent residence here, forming what is known as a "brain drain" in their own countries. In 1990 President Bush signed a bill about granting immigrant visas. The goal of this bill was to increase the number of specially trained workers who will be eligible to take jobs in the United States.

An interesting fact mentioned in *The Globe* article is the increased likelihood of immigrants receiving their doctorates. While they are less likely to be high school graduates than native-born Americans, these newcomers are more than twice as likely to receive their Ph.D.'s than their native-born counterparts.

The Supposed Tax Burden

According to statistics recently published in *The Boston Globe*, newcomers pay $70 billion in annual taxes, earning $285 million in income. Immigrants run a bill of $5.7 billion for public assistance annually, which means that they are putting in far more than they are taking out of the government's funds.

The Double-Standard on Patriotism

We should not expect newly arrived legal immigrants to be extremely patriotic people, when our own citizens lack that same pride.

Many of our European ancestors kept their heritage but also incorporated American customs.

The first American-born Italians were taught English, then Italian, not vice versa. The generations passed, and somehow it seems now that we sons and daughters of immigrant grandparents are less patriotic than our foreign-born ancestors.

Now there are those who condemn legal immigrants for their apparent lack of zeal about speaking English and adopting "American" holidays and customs. But often these immigrants, whose homelands may be riddled by poverty, war, and disease, come to America and see our own lack of patriotism for a country which has wealth, peace, and adequate medical care, and they learn from our mistakes. In short, they follow our bad lead.

"Illegal" Backlash

Legal immigration is not the problem. It is the illegal immigrants whose unchecked invasion has created a backlash, with the legal immigrants becoming scapegoats for this ever-growing problem.

Immigrants who come to America legally want to be here, and it is not for a free ride. They have pride in what they do. They are proud to be Americans, and they want to love this country.

If anybody should be deported, let it be the native-born sons and daughter of immigrants who have lost their passion for America, who complain endlessly about their country and its faults without lifting a hand to make things better. The legal immigrants are thankful for what they have, and what they have is what we take for granted — freedom.

The First and Last Melting Pot

America is the "melting pot" of the world. There is not one dominant race, religion, or sex. Immigration continues to remind us of our ethnic heritage by exposing residents to various cultures, ones we might not have been exposed to if living in a less open society. For the most part, this cultural exposure assists in teaching tolerance and allows for diversity.

If there is ever to be any unity in the world, the United States will be the starting line, for it is the only country where so many people of different races and religions live and work together. After more than three hundred years of success, why should we close our doors?

If immigration benefits America, we see no reason to end it, or even restrict it. At one time we were literally all in the same boat, and as the world's only nation not built upon a common race or religion, the experience of immigration is what unites us all. Let's not allow it to divide us. ≡

(Sources: The Boston Globe, New Grolier Multimedia Encyclopedia, The Statistical Abstract of the United States)

Freedom in Grandma's Hands

Sarah Bairstow
Boston Latin High School

So Much for Us All

Danny Gallagher
Don Bosco Technical High School

Coming to America, the country is so fine.
To give my kids a better life, a better life than mine.

To watch my children play with kids throughout America's land.
Seeing people of different colors walking hand in hand.

My wife is so excited, she's longing to be free.
I'll make my family proud; it's worth it to cross the sea.

The country's rich with jobs flowing free like wine.
The streets are clean, the food is great, the people are so kind.

I'll search for wood and scraps to make my vessel strong.
Three feet wide across and six to eight feet long.

Our raft is very small, but strength it does not lack.
Who could have thought that this great place on us would turn its back?

It took five weeks to get there, five weeks of storms and fear.
But we thought that it was worth it, for now we were safely there.

But the smiles on our faces soon were drenched with tears.
When they told us we were not welcome, horror struck our ears.

As I turned and looked at my children, I wiped their swollen eyes,
Fury filled my mind and soul as I remembered American lies.

My hands began to tremble as I watched my wife's face fall.
So much for the American dream; so much for us all.

Waves of Hope

Evan O'Brien, Catholic Memorial High School

It is a cold, unfeeling day. The savage waves continue to rise and collapse onto our ship. However, the seventh wave is the worst. This is the wave with the most destructive force, this is the wave that kills. Today the ocean shook with the power of God.

Since we left our home, I knew that our voyage would be a hazardous one, but our God has given us the Promised Land, and we will find it.

Brendan, A.D. 588

Legend has it, that for centuries, even before the Norsemen and Vikings, the Irish were out sailing and exploring. They were searching for the Promised Land. Could this land have been North America? The legend tells us that Brendan's journey was a hazardous one. It is said that he encountered demons of fire, floating crystal columns, and a sea creature as large as an island. But his journey was probably not any more dangerous than the journey taken by the millions of Irish immigrants who set sail from their homeland centuries later.

The beauty of Ireland is unimaginable. If one were to look out over the horizon through the mists, before you would be gently rolling, green hills. Ireland has a landscape so rich in beauty and mystery it seems that it would be made for gods. But the Irish are blessed and privileged to be able to experience this beauty. So why would anyone want to leave?

The people did not want to leave Ireland, but they had to. They lived in extreme poverty. Most of the people could not read or write and could not get jobs. Therefore, they could not afford to feed their families. The people desperately tried to escape from "British tyranny." Some people, reluctantly, made their decision to find a better life in America. However, they did not call themselves immigrants, but "exiles." Some were afraid to travel so far and not know what was coming. But they had the courage and perseverance of Brendan. So they set forth for the Promised Land.

Soon the first small waves of immigration lapped against the shores of North America. Even as early as 1621, Irish immigrants had come to this country to settle and to explore. They came looking for independence and wealth. One of the first residents of the Jamestown Colony in Virginia was the Irishman Francis Maguire. Another immigrant, Darby Field, explored the territory north of the Massachusetts Bay Colony. He discovered the White Mountains of New Hampshire.

This small group of immigrants also included farmers, tradesmen, and laborers. They came from well-to-do Irish families as well as impoverished ones. The Irish in the colonies were very sympathetic to the American revolt against the British. These immigrants eventually became volunteer soldiers in America's fight for independence. Irish patriots helped to defend the city of Boston. One of the first men killed at the Boston Massacre was Irishman Patrick Carr. George Washington valued the support of the Irish volunteers. He used the term "St. Patrick" as the password for the troops on March 17, 1776. Among the men who signed the Declaration of Independence were three Irish immigrants. One was a lawyer from Dublin, James Smith; another, George Taylor; and Matthew Thorton, a physician.

Another wave of hope began to crash ashore on the American coast. Immigrants that had already found the Promised Land wrote letters back home to Ireland. These letters tried to persuade other family members to come to America. To people in Ireland, America sounded like paradise. At home in Ireland, the Irish people were enduring hardships. Rents were high and people were evicted from their farms. They had to cut back on their food supply. Farmers who were able to keep their farms could only leave them to one son. This meant that other sons would have to emigrate to find jobs.

An enormous tidal wave washed ashore thousands of desperate Irish. On top of all other hardships came a potato blight, which was caused by a fungus. This famine was so devastating that it destroyed Ireland's major crop. Thousands of people starved to death. Some were found with green stains on their mouths, because they had tried to eat grass in a desperate attempt to save their lives. Disease was rampant. There were outbreaks of typhus, cholera, scurvy, and dysentery. The Great Famine lasted from 1845 to 1850. The most deadly year was 1847. The Irish called it "Black '47." During this year more than 30,000 people died. Many Irish had the choice of starvation or emigration.

Those who chose emigration made a good, but dangerous, decision. There were not even enough ships to carry the emigrants. If you were lucky enough to get aboard one, you were in for the ride of your life! The vessels were old and "unseaworthy." They were manned by poorly trained sailors and captains who gave no thought to their passengers. The ships were rampant with sickness. The crowded holds of the ships were unsanitary and foul smelling. They were so cramped that only children had room to stand. Many ships did not even have enough water. Some ships were able to hold twelve thousand gallons of water, but only carried about eight thousand in leaky barrels. There was very little food and what food there was, was rarely distributed to the passengers. On some "coffin ships" more than forty percent of the passengers died during their hellish voyage.

If you were one of the lucky few to survive the perilous journey to the Promised Land, you would soon find that it did not live up to its promise. Unless the immigrants had friends or relatives waiting for them in America, they had difficulty in finding shelter and jobs. Most of them settled in the cities, often crowded into tenements. Conditions in these tenements were almost as deplorable as those they had left in Ireland and on the coffin ships. In these congested enclaves there were outbreaks of typhoid fever, typhus, and pneumonia. Life here was hardest on the children. Many of them perished before their fifth birthday. Despite these adverse conditions, the Irish tended to stay in tightly knit neighborhoods. In the city of Boston, most of them settled in South Boston or Charlestown.

Many native-born Americans were suspicious of the Irish. America at this time was a nation of Protestant farmers with British ancestors. In contrast, the new immigrants were Catholic, tended to congregate in the cities, and were uneducated. This led to uncertainty and a fear of the Irish. This suspicion made it difficult for the immigrants to find jobs. Being unskilled, they were willing to accept grueling work for very low wages. Nonetheless, they were rejected. Often there were newspaper ads that read, "No Irish need apply."

But the Irish did apply. Throughout the years, they began to settle and become secure with their surroundings. Many of them have participated greatly in making America what it is today. The Irish accepted jobs in construction and worked in mills. They built railroads, canals, streets, and other landmarks of the United States. Brooklyn Bridge and the Statue of Liberty were primarily constructed by Irish immigrants. They also built some of New York's tallest and oldest skyscrapers. Many risked their lives and even died in the process. But they were willing and happy to do it.

From local politician to president of the United States, the Irish have contributed greatly to help strengthen our government. They have looked upon America as the Promised Land, and they have tried to fulfill that title. They have truly made America what it is, "from sea to shining sea."

World Changes

Danny Sullivan, Don Bosco Technical High School

In order to ensure that all people can live and work in a free society, the people must have the proper attitudes to accept one another's cultures. The country's people must realize that not everyone is the same and that we can learn from each other's differences, and accept other cultures. Racism and cultural stereotypes must be done away with so that people may develop their own beliefs and ideas. This will in turn bring about the ideas and beliefs of other cultures so we may learn from their backgrounds. I believe that this will bring racial harmony, because now people would be listening to what's deep down inside. This can only bring about positive effects. All people must have a chance to express what they feel and have a say about what they think about this country, whether it be good or bad.

I think that a society that strives for knowledge and learning about the opinions and ideas of others would ideally bring about people who are more knowledgeable and open. This would also develop a harder working and more productive society. But one major problem may arise and that is one of ignoring one's own culture and family history. So first I suggest people read about their own culture and what significant events happened to their ancestors. It would also be good to trace back one's family tree and see what places a family has moved from or lived in. I think that a country whose population is comprised of a variety of cultures can get along. Then that country will become extremely powerful. Educating a society is the way to achieve this goal and strengthen the culture. But it is important not to force these ideas on people or the nation will erupt into total anarchy. The only way is to teach about different cultures more thoroughly in schools. Then let people develop their own ideas and let them express their beliefs to others. In return, hear the opinions of others. This will advance us as a free country.

Open the Door to Immigrants

Franceine Francis
Boston Latin High School

Dorothy Howard

76 ★ Boston – Our People

Stories, Celebrations, and a Coffee Hour

Beginning the Day in Boston

Dorothy Howard
Boston Latin High School

Baijan Storyteller

Natasha Harvey, Monsignor Ryan Memorial High School

My Baijan aunt, the storyteller. She starts to talk again. She won't get us this time. Her tongue starts moving at the speed of light. Conjuring up ghosts from the past. Spirits of the way things were and specters of the way it should be. Stories so old that if they were trees you could cut them in half and count millions of rings, indicating their age.

Her tongue goes on and on, like a newborn serpent waiting to be fed. The more she talks, the hungrier we are for her story. I sit there listening, eyes bulging out of my sockets, ready to plop on the moist grass and be devoured by the greedy ants below who wait patiently for their feast. This dialect that she speaks is a broken form of my English language. Though I cannot speak it, I understand every word. My American friend sits next to me in awe. Every now and again she squints her eyes as if that will aid her in hearing. She doesn't fully understand the words, though she follows the surprisingly graceful flow of the speaker's powerful thick hands.

She wants us to come closer, but we won't give her that satisfaction. Everyone sits far back, afraid of being accidentally hit by her, yet enthralled by her expressiveness. Like a drowning diver flailing his arms around to gasp for his last breath, her hands go on and on. The more she moves, the more entangled we are in her story. We are still afraid of being hit, but we take that risk as we inch closer and closer. We're practically perched upon her feet like baby birds waiting for worms to be placed in our beaks. We cannot help ourselves. This Baijan snake charmer has won, and she knows it. Now we pay the consequences as she goes in for the kill, finishing up her story. Her tongue moves faster and faster. We are being drowned by the spit that is propelled out of the cave where the tongue lives. She has won.

"Bet you can't win us over again," we yell. We act with false bravado. We know she'll win. She knows she'll win. Regardless, she takes our kamikaze challenge with the eagerness of a resident doctor delivering her first baby. We move back again. She starts to talk. She won't get us this time, this Baijan storyteller.

They Brought Along Their Traditions and Celebrations

Tim Bernstein, Catholic Memorial High School

This is a true story about my great-grandmother Sophie Swerdloff and her journey from Russia to the United States.

About seventy-four years ago a sixteen-year-old girl by the name of Sophie Kossoss was going to her final day of high school in Gomer, Russia, a small town one thousand miles south of Moscow. Sophie was graduating from high school several years in advance, so she could emigrate to the United States with a high school diploma. At that time in Russia there were several social and political issues causing people to leave Russia and emigrate to other countries. The Communists were gaining control and taking over. The atmosphere in the country started to change and Jews became persecuted. Sophie's family was Jewish, which made it very difficult for them. Also there was a lack of food and very few jobs, which made conditions worse. Several years earlier Sophie's father had decided to look for a new land with better opportunity for his family. He emigrated to the United States and settled in New York. Sophie's family decided on the United States because it was known as the golden country and land of opportunity where many jobs were available. The United States also allowed religious freedom and Jews to emigrate. Her father came earlier so he could establish a home for his family and become an American citizen. He became an American citizen before 1919 which was very important for his family. Prior to 1919, if the head of the family became a citizen, then his family automatically gained citizenship, which made it much easier for them when coming to their new home.

In 1923, Sophie Kossoss and her sister boarded a White Star Line ship named the *Homeric* and set off on their journey to the United States of America. Once on the ship, Sophie met a man named Irving Swerdloff, who she thought was very handsome and pleasant. He was bringing his brother and sister along with him to the land of opportunity.

The voyage to America took several long, grueling weeks. Once she arrived she had to say good-bye to her new friend Irving, unknown to her that he would be her future husband. It was a confusing time as Irving had to go to Ellis Island and she did not. Ellis Island is a small island in Upper New York Bay, about three hundred and ninety-six meters east of Jersey City, New Jersey. Between 1892 and 1943 Ellis Island was the major immigration station for the United

States. Many lives were tremendously impacted by what happened on the island as it was there that it was determined whether or not you could enter the United States. Sophie Kossoss didn't have to go to Ellis Island because she was already a citizen, thanks to her father becoming a citizen before 1919. Her father, like many immigrants, thought it was easier and thought there was a better chance of becoming a citizen if only one came at a time, rather than the whole family. Therefore, before 1919 most immigrant families such as the Jews, Irish, Italians, and many others sent the male patriarch to the United States first and the rest of the family followed later.

When Sophie and her sister landed on the mainland, they were immediately picked up by their father and brought back to their new home, an apartment in the Bronx of New York. After settling in her new home, Sophie enrolled in night school to learn to speak English, math, and other customs so she could manage in her new country. English was and still is the language of the United States. Sophie had to learn math because in Europe the metric system is used, while in the United States we use the standard unit of measure. She attended night school for the next four years, while working during the day as a hairdresser on Fifth Avenue.

Several months after Sophie had arrived in the United States, she reunited with Irving while he was working at a barber shop. During the next several years they dated and became close friends. Eventually they married in 1926. For the next six years they worked at their separate jobs until they had saved enough money to open their own business. In 1933 they opened a hair-styling shop on Nagle Street in New York. They worked there together for the next thirty years, until they retired. During that period they had one child, a daughter named Edith, my late grandmother. After retiring, they moved to Lake Louise Marie in the Catskill Mountains of New York State. When people came to the United States, they brought not only themselves but also their traditions and celebrations. An example of this is the Jewish faith that my great-grandmother practices. One holiday or tradition is the festival of lights, better known as Hanukkah. For eight days Jews celebrate by lighting a Menorah, a candle holder that holds eight candles for Hanukkah. They also celebrate by giving family and friends one gift each night of the celebration. Hanukkah usually occurs around the same time as Christmas, which makes for a happy and joyful time for Christians and Jews. ≡

I Was Born in the Year of the Goat

Alice Yu, Brighton High School

Roots are derived from traditions and heritage. Sometimes roots are combined with different cultures. The roots are then blended into something new. One of my traditions can be described as celebration of a new beginning.

The ever-bright incense glowed their fiery image on the enchanting food. Our faces were bright while we gave our respect to the gods and salutation of a new year. The making of the whimsical food and the burning of paper money was offered as a gift to the gods. Afterwards the food was devoured and the ceremony was repeated again at midnight to begin the official Chinese New Year.

Each year has an animal symbol. There are twelve animals cycled through the Chinese zodiac. The zodiac is made up of the rat, buffalo, tiger, rabbit, dragon, snake, horse, goat, monkey, rooster, dog, and pig. Based on tradition, a person who was born in the year of one of these animals will gain the characteristics of that animal perceived from the zodiac.

I was born in the year of the goat, according to the Chinese zodiac. If born in the year of the goat, aesthetics and style revolve around the person's life. The person enjoys being a private person and is compatible with the pig and rabbit. My life somewhat revolves around this perception. At school I am shy; on the other hand, at home I am not. I have friends who are noble, talented, and affectionate.

According to Chinese traditions, the year I was born affects my life. But I still have other characteristics, not perceived from the zodiac. Therefore, there must be another influence for my roots. America provided me with an environment where I could interact with people of different cultures. The people come together to celebrate one of America's traditions, the New Year. It is celebrated with fireworks, party hats and whistles, and the giving of New Year resolutions.

My roots are like materials mixed in a crucible. Traditions and heritage are the materials in the crucible. The fire under the crucible is America. It allows the materials to mix together and form a new kind of substance. This new substance is made up of my Chinese traditions and heritage and of my American experience and life. I am Chinese-American. ≡

African Ancestry and Togetherness

Cassandra Pauyo, St. Clare Central High School

I called my friend up the other day and told her I was doing a report on Kwanzaa. I know she celebrates Kwanzaa at her home. I asked her to describe her experience. I know many things about this custom; but when she described it, I felt as if I was experiencing it. She is of African descent. Kwanzaa is a celebration of African ancestry and of togetherness with your family. This custom means a lot to her because she is very family oriented, just as I am.

Kwanzaa reminds her to be a better person each year. The seven principles of Kwanzaa help you to learn, achieve, and grow as a person. A couple of years ago I went to her house a few days before the Kwanzaa celebration, which is December 26 through January 2, and saw many different colored candles. Finally, I've realized what they are for.

Seven candles represent the seven principles. One is lighted each day, a black candle in the center for the richness of the skin, three green candles for success, and three red candles for the hardships faced during the year. At her house everyone wakes up at four o'clock in the morning and watches the candle for the principle of the day being lighted. Before lighting the candle, her father says a prayer for each person individually, so that they may be blessed with that principle.

The first principle, *umoja,* is unity. The black candle is lighted. At her house on that day, no one is to watch television, listen to the radio, or talk on the telephone. Her family sits around for hours just talking, telling stories, and simply enjoying each other's company.

The second principle, *kujichagulia,* is self-determination. A red candle is lighted. Her mother braids her hair in a fancy African style. She loves the way her hair looks. She looks like an African princess. Her mother tells her that that is exactly who she is. That makes her feel extremely proud.

The third principle, *ujima,* is responsibility. A green candle is lighted. Everyone works together to do a family chore, painting the kitchen. She has fun mixing the paint and experimenting with different colors. Her family has fun working together doing a tough and tedious job. I was amazed by this.

The fourth principle, *ujamaa,* is being economically conscious. A red candle is lighted. When you enter the kitchen of her home, there is a box in the corner full of money. During the year everyone puts money in this box, and when this day arrives, they buy a family gift: this year a computer! Also on this day they start saving all over again for next year.

The fifth principle, *nia*, is purpose. A green candle is lighted. This day is about dreaming of your future. My friend wants to be an architect, so she designed and constructed a dog house out of wood.

The sixth principle, *kuumba*, is creativity. A red candle is lighted. She and her brother have created a dance to present to the family. Their dance tells a story of how Kwanzaa originated.

The seventh principle, *imani*, is faith. A green candle is lighted. Her family prays for almost three hours. They ask God to give them the belief that good things will happen.

After praying, they have a big meal consisting of vegetables, fruits, rice, yams, manioc, okra, plantains, collard greens, and fish. I don't practice the Kwanzaa celebration at my home; however, I try to practice each of the seven principles.

I would encourage others to look into practicing these principles because we could not only become better people and a better world, but also we would not have as many problems as we do. ≡

Join Together for a Great Team

Tam Nguyen
Thomas Edison Middle School

Acknowledgments

The Boston Public Library Foundation wishes to express its gratitude to the many people who joined together to make the fourth annual collaborative program with Boston's public, parochial, and private schools an overwhelming success.

Boston Public Schools

Dr. Thomas Payzant, Superintendent

Janice Jackson, Deputy Superintendent

Martha Gillis, Reading Coordinator

Jean Dorcus, Betty Royston, and Kathy Tosolini

Boston Parochial Schools

Sister Ann Dominic Roach, OP, Superintendent, Archdiocese of Boston

Sister Bernadette Bell, RSM, and Sister Ann Moore, CND

Boston Public Library Trustees

William O. Taylor, President; Pamela Seigle, Vice President

The Honorable William M. Bulger, Libby Chiu, V. Paul Deare, Donna DePrisco, Berthé M. Gaines, David McCullough, and Joseph E. Mullaney

Staff: Arthur Curley, Liam Kelly, Lesley Loke, and Jane Manthorne

Boston Public Library Foundation Board of Directors

Kevin C. Phelan, Chairman; Prudence S. Crozier, Vice Chairman;

Nader F. Darehshori, President

Paula Alvary, Joel B. Alvord, Lawrence A. Bianchi, Arnold Bloom, Leo R. Breitman, Robin A. Brown, Lewis Burleigh, The Honorable William M. Bulger, Greg C. Carr, Libby Chiu, James F. Cleary, Diddy Cullinane, John J. Cullinane, V. Paul Deare, Donna DePrisco, Lawrence S. DiCara,

James S. DiStasio, Gerard F. Doherty, Ed Eskandarian, Katherine W. Fanning, Robert P. Fitzgerald, Charles Fox, Robert B. Fraser, Berthé M. Gaines, Carol R. Goldberg, Richard Harter, Alice Hennessey, Ronald A. Homer, Jackie Jenkins-Scott, Elizabeth A. Johnson, Hubert E. Jones, Paul A. LaCamera, Alan LeBovidge, Peter S. Lynch, Thomas J. May, David McCullough, Cathy E. Minehan, Joseph E. Mullaney, Paul C. O'Brien, David E. Place, Neil L. Rudenstine, Jeffrey B. Rudman, Michael R. Sandler, Elaine Schuster, Pamela Seigle, David C. Shanks, William M. Shiebler, Susan F. Smith, Micho F. Spring, Ira Stepanian, Jacqueline Stepanian, Earl Tate, and Robert E. Wise

Staff: Karyn Wilson, Blake Jordan, and Tara Evin

Sponsors

The Birmingham Foundation, NYNEX New England, and State Street Bank

Supporters

Thanks to Jack Pow of John P. Pow Printing Company for donating the printing services for this publication, Lou Nickinello and Lois Catanzaro of Ackerley Communications for the donation of 200 billboards throughout Greater Boston neighborhoods to display winning middle-school billboard entries, and Paul A. LaCamera, Elizabeth Cheng, and Ramsay Gifford-Trusell of Channel 5 WCVB-TV for creating a special video for classroom study.

Publisher

A special thanks to Nader F. Darehshori, Chairman, President, and Chief Executive Officer, Houghton Mifflin Company, and his talented staff led by Jane Muse for publishing *Boston — Our People...Coming to America*. Sarah Ambrose designed the book and cover and handled the production, and Margaret Kearney provided editorial support. They were assisted by Patricia English and Robin Murphy. A special thank-you to Jane Manthorne, emerita, Boston Public Library, for her editorial review and type composition of the essays, poems, and other submissions.